NATURAL
REMEDIES
FOR YOUR CAT

NATURAL
REMEDIES
FOR YOUR CAT

Christopher Day
MA, VetMB, MRCVS, VetFFHom

Illustrated by
Anuk Naumann

PICCADILLY PRESS
London

Designed by Dalia Hartman
Printed and bound by Bath Press Ltd, Avon, for the publishers
Piccadilly Press Ltd., 5 Castle Road, London NW1 8PR

ISBN: 1 85340 265 6

AUTHOR AND PUBLISHER'S NOTE:
If symptoms persist or any remedy causes adverse effects, it is advisable to
seek assistance from a professional practitioner.
Neither the publisher nor the author is responsible for the efficacy or
suitability for any particular cat of any of the remedies or cures set out in
this book. Whenever dealing with matters of health it is vital that a proper
diagnosis is made and professional advice is sought at the appropriate time.

Christopher Day is a qualified veterinary surgeon who uses alternative
medicine almost exclusively. As well as running his own practice in
Oxfordshire, he is actively involved in
teaching and research with natural medicine and is Hon. Secretary of
the British Association of Homoeopathic Veterinary Surgeons. He has
written a number of books on alternative medicine for animals but
this is his first one for Piccadilly Press.

Anuk Naumann also lives in Oxfordshire. She qualified as an architect
before turning to art. She paints in watercolour and has held
exhibitions all over the country.

ACKNOWLEDGEMENTS

It is with great gratitude that I acknowledge Caroline
Beaney's very hard work in grappling with my manu-
script. I also thank Brenda Gardner of Piccadilly Press
for her untiring cajoling along the way and her asking
me to write this book in the first place. To all the staff
at Piccadilly I give thanks for their patience and for
incorporating my handwritten modifications.

DEDICATION

To all my feline friends who have helped me to learn
about natural medicine and the innate self-healing
power of the body, so often underestimated. Also, to
all my veterinary friends around the world who have
been a source of inspiration.

INTRODUCTION

This book is intended to provide the reader with a guide to easy-to-use remedies for common cat ailments. It is *not* intended to substitute for proper veterinary care, should this be required, whether that care is supplied by a veterinarian using "alternative" or "conventional" methods.

The reader is strongly advised to seek veterinary help whenever the symptoms appear worrying or whenever in doubt. It is also advisable that treatments taken from this book should not be used over long periods without effect, since that would involve a delay in seeking effective and necessary treatment elsewhere.

Some key dietary factors are mentioned at times however there is not enough space for adequate comments on diet, accommodation or life-style. It is clear, however, that these aspects are fundamental to health and should be very carefully considered. A short discussion of these points follows.

NUTRITION AND LIFESTYLE

In general terms cats are best outdoors and hunting.
This "natural" way of life, so ideally suited to the cat's
nature, may, however, be a hazard to the cat itself, from
traffic, dogs, birds of prey or other cats; a hazard to
the environment (e.g. a neighbour's garden); a hazard
to wildlife since wild creatures are the target of the
hunt (a cat is no discriminator between those species
we consider rare, desirable and attractive and those we
may consider commonplace and of nuisance value).
Cats will adapt well to being kept indoors and confined
to barracks, so long as the room is made interesting for
them, if there is adequate daylight (full-spectrum
lighting may be very helpful to health), if a clean litter
tray is available at all times, if water is on access and if
a scratching post is supplied. Indoor or outdoor, the
cat keeper must decide, but if the cat is given the
choice, most would opt for free access to outdoors.
Regular grooming and looking at eyes, ears, mouth, skin
etc. are essential and clearly a loving home is important
to well-being. No hearth scene is complete without a
contented, curled-up cat soaking up the warmth.

Cats are very self-reliant but also highly intuitive and able to form a very close and dynamic bond with human companions. This is one of the many reasons we keep them. I'm sure they can even act as a "conductor" of our stresses and discomforts, often to their own health detriment. Cats have been variously revered, held in suspicion, adored and respected by man in a unique fashion down the ages, not least for their paradoxical affection combined with aloofness. In his *Just So Stories* Rudyard Kipling writes of "The Cat That Walks Alone". This is the self-sufficiency, self-reliance and exploitive nature of the cat.

Cats are not big drinkers, owing to their desert origins, but access to water is essential. Spring water or well water, not from plastic bottles is best. Most cats shun getting wet but a Turkish Van will revel in a bath! Kidney health depends, apart from a healthy diet, upon a good water supply.

DIET

By and large natural, fresh and raw food is best for cats. Our modern habit of supermarket shopping with everything for convenience out of a can or bag may not be a healthy development. Manufactured food gains from being "scientifically formulated" which means, if we assume science has all the answers, that all your cat's needs will be contained therein. However, on the negative side, scientists are humans and will inevitably make errors of omission and of commission. These compound each other. In addition, processed foods suffer from denaturation, potentially harmful additives, unnatural consistency, lack of variety and allow the cat no ability to select according to its perceived daily requirements. A cat is an obligate carnivore which means it cannot survive totally without meat or meat products. Salmonella food-poisoning is an ever-present risk for cats, which are very susceptible to this disease. Fresh is therefore best. Raw is also best but the risk of parasites such as tapeworms is thereby increased. Cats in the wild will take their meat live and with bone, skin, fur, bowel contents etc. This is not reproducible in any other way. Everything we do to vary this is a compromise.

Suitable dietary components are raw meat, raw freshwater fish (which can be fed whole but freshly caught), lightly baked or steamed white fish, oily fish (e.g. fresh mackerel, fresh sardines etc.), organic chicken, wild rabbit, seaweed, wholegrain cereals, finely chopped or grated raw ground vegetables and herbs (such as parsley, mint, burnet, lettuce, dandelion, cress, celery, thyme), small quantities of organic liver or other offal, vegetable oil (such as sunflower or sesame), raw eggs, sprouted grains and seeds, cottage cheese, sprouted pulses etc. Because a cat's digestive system is not well-adapted to coping with raw vegetable material (ingesta from prey normally provides the vegetable ingredients pre-digested), all vegetable material must be very finely broken down for them. Hypoallergenic, well-prepared vitamin and mineral supplements without additives such as flavourings, colourings and preservatives fill any gaps if you are in doubt, but quantities of "force fed" minerals and vitamins must be carefully monitored to avoid the risk of over-supply. The reader will note reference to organic material in the foregoing text. This is because non-organic material is infinitely more likely to contain residues of potentially harmful and undesirable chemicals. "Free-range" is not sufficient as feeding methods are rife with added chemicals. Broiler chickens and rabbits are kept in undesirable conditions and often require the support of antibiotics to keep them alive. Food from them is more likely to contain antibiotic residues (as an example) and the system of management should not benefit from the encouragement of patronage.

On the subject of residues, if organic food supplies are not available (Demeter or Soil Association symbol approved) then parts of an animal's body most likely to concentrate harmful residues will be liver, kidney and fat. Bear this in mind when feeding animal products to your cat.

The author advises the use of feeding bowls and water bowls which are impermeable and not prone to wear and tear by the cat's tongue (i.e. use steel or glazed pottery bowls for instance rather than plastic which may give rise to the ingestion of plastic and colourants).

VACCINATION

No one wants their cat to suffer any of the major infectious diseases such as Influenza (Calici, Rhinotracheitis etc.), Enteritis (Panleucopaenia), Leukosis (FeLV or FLV), Immunodeficiency (FIV), Chlamydia, Peri- tonitis (FIP), Anæmia (FIA). Conventional vaccines are available for the first three of these and for Chlamydia. (Rabies vaccination is not allowed in the UK at the time of writing.)

A cat's immune system is a very finely poised and delicately balanced yet powerful entity in the daily battle for life and health. Although it has been shown (sadly by the use of laboratory cats) that vaccination is able to increase specific immunity to the four diseases for which vaccine is as yet available, what is not widely discussed is the vaccine's potential ability to disturb or even damage the cat's immune system generally. There is no way to assess vaccine-susceptibility so far as we know and some cats are very much more sensitive to such influences than others. Deaths, severe illness and chronic mild illness (including skin problems, sinus problems etc.) have all been recorded as following closely on vaccination.

There is an alternative to conventional vaccination but it has not been efficacy-tested on laboratory animals. No *proof* of efficacy therefore exists. However, many breeders, show people, cat lovers and catteries now feel strongly that the alternative is as effective as, and safer than, conventional vaccination. This alternative is the use of homoeopathic nosodes. Nosodes are available for *all* the aforementioned infectious diseases, not just the "big three". They are given orally by the owner and have no side-effects. Many outbreaks of FLV, FIV, FIP etc. in cat colonies seem to have been stopped in their tracks by this means. Cats with early stages of these diseases (usually considered fatal and without chance of cure) have been helped to recovery by these medicines alongside full homoeopathic prescribing.

It is now, sadly, almost impossible to obtain pedigree kittens which have not been given initial vaccinations. This is done for the best motives but is not always in the kitten's best interests. The author's own animals are not vaccinated but are given homoeopathic prevention methods only and are meeting cats from all over the country daily. When vaccinations are made compulsory we unfortunately lose the freedom of choice. Hopefully, enough clinical research data will emerge in the fullness of time to verify the present apparent findings of the author and others and authenticate them.

If you do wish to purchase nosodes for the prevention of infectious diseases in your cats, you are strongly advised to purchase them only from a qualified veterinary surgeon who alone can give you the proper advice and verify the source of the medicine and its quality for you. If possible seek the help and advice of one with the postgraduate homoeopathic qualification. These veterinarians have received teaching on the subject. There are many pitfalls in using other sources.

If we ignore for now the obvious monetary advantage to manufacturer and retailer in selling vaccines for cats, there is still tremendous pressure put upon the cat keeper to vaccinate since veterinarians are motivated to prevent disease wherever possible. Most know nothing of homoeopathic nosodes so it is down to you, the reader, to try to glean as much information and understanding as possible and make a decision accordingly. The welfare of your cat is your responsibility in the final instance.

Apart from vaccination/nosode considerations the health and resistance of your cat to infectious diseases is affected very favourably by diet, ventilation and lifestyle factors, as discussed previously. Always purchase/obtain your cat from a healthy source if possible and keep and feed him/her as naturally as possible.

WORMS AND FLEAS

There are sections of the text of this book given over to these important everyday problems under the headings of ROUNDWORMS, TAPEWORMS and SKIN PROBLEMS. In general terms there is a constant dilemma between choosing very effective but often very toxic modern chemicals and those more natural compounds which involve a little more work and concentration in exchange for their greater safety. Organophosphorus compounds, for instance, are particularly dangerous, and insidiously so, but are widely available in flea collars and flea sprays. The reader must make as good a choice as possible but must make efforts to be informed on the relative dangers and advantages of each available method. One can do worse than feed brewers yeast and garlic to a cat on a daily basis; these act as wholesome deterrents and are readily available. Brewers yeast can even be applied to a cat's coat. Modern developments of spot-on chemicals and chemicals for the cat to ingest in order to render fleas infertile are very recent players on the scene and the reader must decide between the natural approach and methods as yet not time-honoured nor proven safe over long periods (see also pages 92, 97, 102).

THE REMEDIES

Natural medicine is for the most part the art of stimulating the body's innate healing powers. These are often, in our modern and mechanistic world, underestimated and neglected. The immense and often unrespected power of natural medicine is attributed to the strong desire and ability of the body to be well.

A short discussion of each of the natural therapies mentioned in the text follows but it is worthwhile drawing attention to one or two points first.

Homoeopathic remedies are delicate and rely upon subtle influences upon the body. Strong-smelling substances may overthrow their effect so essential oils should not, as a general rule, be used at the same time as homoeopathic dosing and may even be counter-productive if given in conjunction with intercurrent homoeopathic treatment (see discussion on essential oils to follow).

Herbal remedies contain material quantities of chemicals,

some of which are of dubious safety if given for prolonged periods. Consult an expert if in doubt but, in general, do not give for longer than one week without obvious beneficial effect.

The different therapies are discussed and mentioned in the treatment section in order to be able to allow the reader to select an appropriate treatment most suitable to his or her circumstances. Different households have different traditions and stocks of medicines will reflect this. It is hoped that everyone will find something of value and use in these pages.

HOMOEOPATHY

This system of medicine is based on the principle that "like cures like". Remedies are given in diseases which have been shown to be able to produce symptoms in a healthy body most similar to those seen in the disease. The system was formally discovered and developed in humans by Samuel Hahnemann in Germany during the late eighteenth and early nineteenth centuries. Animals now benefit from this.

Remedies are taken from plant, animal or mineral

material and are usually diluted to extreme levels, rendering them very safe indeed. The dilution is referred to as *potentisation* since, after the meticulous processes used, the dilution of the remedy paradoxically renders it more powerful as a medicine.
The "potency" of the medicine is a function of its dilution so 6c and 30c are diluted "one in one hundred" six times and thirty times respectively. Decimal potencies are similar, taking steps of "one in ten" dilution and are denoted by x, e.g.: 3x, 6x.

The potency 6c is more readily obtainable than 30c. Even higher potencies can be obtained from manufacturers and some pharmacies. Actual dosage in numbers of tablets or drops given is not related to body size - a mouse or elephant can receive the same dose!

Frequency of dosing is set according to the severity of the problem. Sudden, severe disease requires frequent dosing, perhaps as often as every half hour until symptoms start to subside . Less serious or slower onset problems require less frequent dosing, say once or twice daily. Chronic, long-standing conditions require only sporadic dosing. Guides to frequency given in the text must be taken as that only, i.e. a rough guide to be varied by the reader according to circumstance.

Sometimes, there is a desire to give more than one

remedy. By and large, this is not a good idea since it does reduce the effect of homoeopathy. However, if it is deemed necessary to give more than one remedy concurrently, it is advisable to give them on separate dosing occasions and in different potencies. Individualisation is very important in the selection of homoeopathic remedy, but is too large a subject for this book.

HERBS

Herbal remedies are taken from plant material and contain actual quantities of chemicals from the plants. They are not diluted as in homoeopathy. For this reason, some caution in their use is prudent. However, they are very safe if used in the correct context and not overdosed in quantity given or duration applied. The active principles are delivered in combination with many other substances thus often providing synergistic beneficial effects or even preventing harmful effects.

Herbal medicine is as old as human civilisation itself, all human cultures developing their own indigenous plant medicine lore. Conventional drug medicine owes many of its discoveries to original herbal medicines. However, the safety of the "whole context" of the plant is removed and the chemicals have usually been modified in the laboratory.

Infusions of herbs are made by pouring boiling water over plant material in a pot. A teaspoon of herbs can be used per teacupful made. A teacupful will generally supply a cat with ten doses of herbal medicine.

Tinctures or powders of herbs can be purchased and are a convenient method of storage. However, it is not always easy to persuade a cat to take herbal medication, particularly if there is alcohol in the liquid. Tinctures are therefore best diluted in water and given to the cat by means of a syringe or teaspoon introduced very gently into the side of the mouth. Two or three drops of tincture or a small pinch of powdered material usually constitutes a feline dose.

Herbal remedies can be mixed, often with advantage.

ESSENTIAL OILS (AROMATHERAPY)

Apart from the use of herbs to make medicines as described under homoeopathy and herbs, there is a third way in which their curative properties can be harnessed. That is by distillation of their essential oils.

These oils are aromatic and can be used in a number of ways. Oils can be heated over a flame in an aromatic diffuser or vaporiser, thus pervading an enclosed space such as a room with their medical virtues. Care must, of course, be taken to ensure a cat cannot knock over a burning vaporiser. STEAM INHALATION is a practical course of action with cats whereby five or so drops of oil can be added to a bowl of hot water in front of a cat cage and a sheet put over both the bowl and the cage to ensure breathing of the vapour. Alternatively, oils can be applied directly and sparingly to the skin or ear opening for problems therein and can even be massaged in gently over joints in the case of sprains. Care should be taken, however, since some of the oils are very strong indeed and can make delicate skin sore.

It is not advised to give the oils by mouth, or to put them in the eyes or nose.

Strong-smelling oils such as CAMPHOR, BLACK PEPPER, EUCALYPTUS or MINT, should not be used with ho- moeopathic treatments.

For safety reasons, do not use essential oils in pregnant queens.

Multiple prescriptions of essential oils can be given on occasions, if deemed necessary to the case.

BACH FLOWER REMEDIES

A further way of harnessing medical properties of plants was pioneered by Edward Bach in the 1930s. He developed a system using 38 remedies. These remedies are valuable in helping the mind of man and animals to overcome its problems and, via this route, can also treat physical disease.

The remedies are prepared from the flowers of wild plants, bushes and trees and their curative energy is extracted either by standing a bowl of water containing floating flowers in sunlight for three hours or by a boiling method.

Remedies are stored in alcohol and water and may be given diluted in much the same way as herbal tinctures.

Multiple prescriptions of Bach Flower remedies are often given together, with no apparent loss of efficacy. In fact, it is often to be recommended. However, as a guide, I suggest not putting more than five in any given mixture.

BIOCHEMIC TISSUE SALTS

In 1873 a German physician - William Schuessler from Oldenburg - proposed a system of medicine based on 12 inorganic or mineral salts which are constituents of living cells. He based his theories on the fact that if the cells of the body function normally, then the body will be healthy. His "12 Tissue Salts" and the many combinations of these which are possible are prepared by the same method of trituration and potentisation as homoeopathic mineral remedies (q.v.), usually to a potency of 6x. Their medical function is obtained by exploiting the regulatory and modulatory ability of substances in "potency" thereby normalising cell function and bringing about health.

The tissue salts may safely be used in conjunction with other therapies and combinations, of up to five tissue salts, are often used. The tablets are very friable and easily broken down to powder or may be readily dissolved directly in the cat's mouth or in a little water first. Intolerance to milk sugar (of which the tablets are made) is the only contraindication.

ABRASIONS
(see Injury)

ABSCESS

When cats fight they often manage to part without
injury, one assuming dominance. However, this is not
always the case and when there is injury, this is inflicted

ABSCESS (continued)

by claws or teeth or both. Cats' claws and teeth are notorious for harbouring very dangerous, pus-forming bacteria and an abscess usually follows. As long as there is no bony damage the result is usually more painful than serious but it creates an ugly and extremely painful swelling. In due course this will burst but help can be needed.

Bathing with warm, strong, SALTY WATER can be very soothing and helps to "draw" the abscess.

Internally, the homoeopathic medicine HEPAR SULPHURIS 6c is very beneficial. It helps the process, thereby reducing the duration of the problem and it soothes as a result of its healing action, ensuring that the cat has fully isolated the "invasion" within the abscess. There is usually a prompt and dramatic reduction in pain. Suggested dose: one tablet four times daily for three days. SILICA 30c will help if an old abscess has failed to resolve. One tablet daily for a week will usually suffice.

Herbal remedies can also be called in to help. ECHINACEA is the most important of these and a useful dose is one teaspoonful of fresh root in a cup of water and bring it to the boil, simmer it for 10 minutes and then give one ml twice daily. GARLIC is also an extremely effective internal antiseptic.

If the cat is very distressed, a few drops of BACH'S RESCUE REMEDY twice on the first day will help to defuse the situation.

ACNE

This is a term used to describe the crusts which form on the skin on the end of the lower jaw under a cat's chin. It can be very troublesome to cure.

Homoeopathically there is no specific remedy but the correct *constitutional* remedy is bound to help. This may be GRAPHITES, NATRUM MUR. or SULPHUR.

Herbal tinctures and internal medicines can be very effective. A mixture of CLEAVERS and BURDOCK internally twice daily over a period of four weeks. A tincture can be made from CLEAVERS (Galium aparine) and bathed on the area once daily.

BACH RESCUE CREAM can be applied once daily in addition to this.

ACNE (continued)

Tissue Salts: KALI. SULPH. or CALC. SULPH. may help this condition or consider a combination of CALC. SULPH., KALI. MUR., KALI. SULPH., SILICA.

ALLERGY

Allergy is not commonly a clear diagnosis in cats. It may be defined as abnormal functioning of the immune system, following on sensitisation to foreign protein material. Sensitisation may occur following on many adverse stimuli to the immune system such as viruses, poisoning or even, sometimes, vaccination. The very sudden and severe form is called Anaphylaxis (q.v.) and may occur after injection of antibiotics or vaccines. Flea-bite allergy plays a part in the ætiology of miliary eczema or miliary dermatitis (q.v.).

ALOPECIA

This term indicates loss of hair and is usually used to describe conditions in which there is no pain, irritation or obvious inflammation. It is usually hormonal in origin, occurring mostly in spayed or castrated cats. It can be quite difficult to treat. However some remedies have been used successfully.

The homoeopathic remedies ARSENICUM 6c and NATRUM MUR. 6c once daily are very helpful remedies. The preparation PITUITARY GLAND 6c is a very useful basic treatment. Also FOLLICULINUM 30c or TESTOSTERONE 30c depending upon the sex of the cat may also help. These last three should be taken twice weekly.

Herbally, EVENING PRIMROSE OIL is an excellent aid in the treatment of alopecia as, too, is KELP.

Aromatherapy can be of enormous value in this condition, CALAMUS OIL being a very effective stimulant to the skin. Calamus is considered a little strong or even dangerous by some authors so it can be replaced by HORSERADISH, CLARY SAGE, YARROW, or ROSEMARY, all of which can stimulate hair regrowth.

ANAEMIA

Anæmia is a condition characterised by loss of red blood cells or hæmoglobin. It can follow on serious infective diseases such as FLV and FIA but can also be the result of injury or chronic illness. The membranes of eye and mouth will usually appear pale.

Iron supplementation, probably best supplied by a mixture of NETTLES, KELP and PARSLEY is essential. Homoeopathically we think of CHINA 30c or FERRUM PHOS. 30c as very good stimuli to the body to help it restore the blood. Give once daily.

Tissue salts: CALC. PHOS. is the principal remedy to aid production of new red cells. FERR. PHOS. may also help.

If anæmia is the result of hæmorrhage, then clearly blood loss must be halted (see bleeding).

ANAPHYLAXIS

This is a sudden, violent and very dangerous form of allergic disease. It is an occasional sequel of vaccination or antibiotic injection. The symptoms are inco-ordination, salivation, and possible collapse. If severe enough it can result in death. Rapid treatment is essential. If there is no very rapid relief by giving these remedies it is essential to seek veterinary help. How-ever, it is constructive to use these gentle and valuable remedies while *en route* to the veterinary surgeon.

ACONITUM 200c is the best homoeopathic remedy. If there is swelling of the face and membranes in the mouth are dry, APIS MELLIFICA 30c may be a useful homoeopathic remedy. Give as often as ten times in the first half hour or until symptoms subside, if earlier.

Bach RESCUE REMEDY may also be of value. It is very difficult to dose with herbal remedies when the cat is in a collapsed state but aromatic oils of PEPPERMINT or THYME could be of value, placed near the nose.

ANTIBIOTICS

In some cases, cats which receive antibiotics react badly. A sudden and drastic response is anaphylaxis (q.v.). However, less dramatic responses can occur and even chronic problems such as injection site swelling,

ANTIBIOTICS (continued)

abscessation, diarrhoea, etc. can follow.

The homoeopathic medicine ALOE 30c is very effective
when diarrhoea occurs. Should there be facial swelling
APIS MELLIFICA 30c may help, painful swelling at site of
injection requires HEPAR SULPHURIS 30c and chronic
abscessation requires SILICA 30c. Silica should be
given once daily and the others up to four times daily
depending on severity.

Probiotics e.g. LACTOBACILLUS or BIFIDUS may help
digestive disturbances following on antibiosis. VITA-
MIN B and C should also be given as an aid to recovery.

ANXIETY

Cats can be anxious creatures under certain circumstances and gentle, natural remedies can be of
immense help.

Homoeopathic ACONITE 30c will help in times of
panic, ARGENTUM NITRICUM 200c or GELSEMIUM 200c
may help if there is anticipatory anxiety. PULSATILLA

30c will often suit the generally anxious cat. These remedies may be given once or twice at the start of the situation or half an hour before anticipated situations.

Herbally, SKULLCAP, VALERIAN, PASSIFLORA or CHAMOMILE can all serve to soothe and relax. Tinctures or infusions are best.

Tissue Salts: KALI. PHOS. is most likely to be helpful under such circumstances.

LAVENDER and LEMON BALM essential oils have an undisputed effect on anxiety.

Bach RESCUE REMEDY is of proven value, a drop or two often providing rapid relief. AGRIMONY can also help.

APPETITE

Loss of appetite can be a sign of serious illness so veterinary help should be sought if in doubt.

However, if it is only of non-serious causation, homoeo-pathic NUX VOMICA 30c may help. A variable appetite may indicate PULSATILLA 30c. A depraved appetite could call for PHOSPHORUS 30c. Give once daily for three days.

Herbally, infusions of CASCARA, LIQUORICE or GINGER can help to promote a healthy appetite and to aid peristalsis and digestion.

NAT. PHOS. is the Biochemic Tissue Salt to consider in cases of poor appetite.

Essential oils of BERGAMOT and CARAWAY can provide very valuable help in restoring a fickle appetite.

Nutritionally, VITAMIN B1 (or Thiamine) supplementation can provide a useful stimulus to appetite.

ARTHRITIS

This sometimes crippling disease of the joints is not common in cats.

Vitamin C provides a useful nutritional aid in the treatment of arthritis, as can cod liver oil in moderation.

Homoeopathically RHUS TOX. 6c can help when pains and stiffness seem to be worse as the cat arises from sleeping. Give one tablet three times daily for ten days. Sporadic treatment may be necessary thereafter.

However, there are many herbs which can be of help in ameliorating symptoms. DEVIL'S CLAW, CLEAVERS, BURDOCK, COMFREY or BONESET are perhaps the most widely used.

BACK PROBLEMS

Cats may need careful and skilled chiropractic help,
just as humans do from time to time. Cats are very
agile and nimble creatures but a wrong move can result
in a missed foothold and the inco-ordinated reflex
response can cause misalignment of spine or pelvis.
Similarly, accidents of all kinds can disrupt the back.
Veterinary care will be needed if there are severe

problems, particularly if bowel or bladder function is affected.

ARNICA 6c and RUTA 6c are homoeopathic remedies of great value under such circumstances. If nerve problems or even paralysis follow, HYPERICUM 6c is an invaluable aid to healing and to pain reduction. One tablet four times daily will provide some relief.

Herbal COMFREY is a great help in any injury.

Acupuncture can be a very effective treatment and should be carried out by a veterinary surgeon.

BAD BREATH (Halitosis)

Bad breath can result from illnesses affecting liver or kidney and can therefore herald serious disease. Also, gum disease and tooth disease can lead to this problem. If your cat is ill or if signs persist, veterinary advice should be sought. However, natural measures to help bad breath are:

Homoeopathic MERCURIUS SOLUBILIS 30c once daily

BAD BREATH (continued)

can be a great help if the mouth is wet and if gums are swollen.

Herbally, the following should help: ECHINACEA tincture, two drops twice daily. GARLIC supplement. CHLORO-PHYLL tablets - one taken twice daily. PARSLEY, PEPPERMINT or FENUGREEK infusions will help to freshen the breath and aid digestion. DILL seeds ground into a powder and applied to the gums can aid oral freshness and hygiene.

BALANCE PROBLEMS

This can usually indicate an ear infection. Ear mite infestation may be a root cause of the problem. In this case and in the case of bacterial infection, if natural methods of control fail, veterinary help is strongly advised sooner rather than later (see Canker).

Homoeopathically, CAUSTICUM 30c or HEPAR SULPHURIS 30c can be a great aid to healing and restoring normal balance. Three or four times daily dosing is beneficial.

ROSEMARY, JUNIPER, LAVENDER and THYME are all

essential oils of great help in ear problems. Apply a tiny quantity beside the ear opening. If the oils are too strong for your cat's skin, dilute with a little almond or safflower oil.

BEREAVEMENT

Like humans, cats feel the loss of a much-loved feline or human companion.

Homoeopathic IGNATIA 200c or NATRUM MUR. 200c can help enormously to restore *joie de vivre*. These can be given once daily for a week. Anxiety and excitability call for IGNATIA, depression calls for NAT. MUR.

Herbal LIME BLOSSOM infusion can provide relief from depression following on the loss of a beloved companion.

BERGAMOT, ORANGE BLOSSOM and LAVENDER oils serve to soothe the mental effects of loss.

Bach Flower remedies such as STAR OF BETHLEHEM or CHICORY can help regain mental balance. A few drops twice daily are all that is usually required.

BIRTH

Natural birth can be aided by a number of different natural therapies. Remember to call a veterinary surgeon if birth is protracted.

Homoeopathic CAULOPHYLLUM 30c given six times at three day intervals from three weeks prior to the expected time of birth usually provides valuable assistance.

Herbally RASPBERRY LEAVES have a long tradition in aiding tone of womb muscle and assisting labour.

Essential oils of JASMINE, CLARY SAGE and TRUE LAVEN-DER will provide added support at the time of birth.

BITES
(see Abscess)

BLEEDING

In general, cats do not suffer badly from hæmorrhage.
If hæmorrhage is serious, seek veterinary advice.
Remedies worth remembering, should the need arise,
are however:

Homoeopathic ARNICA 30c, IPECACUANHA 30c and
HAMAMELIS 6c. One of these can be given, and
repeated at short intervals, until bleeding stops.

Herbally, YARROW, BURR MARIGOLD, WITCH HAZEL
and COMFREY can be very useful in controlling bleeding. Tinctures or infusions can be made of these herbs.

After bleeding you may need to refer to the Anæmia
section, to help restore the blood loss.

BOIL
(see Abscess)

BONE INJURY

The healing of bone injury can be hastened and improved by natural remedies. This does not substitute the need for correct immobilisation of fractures.

Homoeopathically, SYMPHYTUM 6x, ARNICA 30c and CALCAREA FLUOR. 6c can be given twice daily. ARNICA will help the immediate effects and allay shock. SYMPHYTUM and CALC. FLUOR. will help the long-term healing process.

Herbally, COMFREY is the best known treatment.

BRUISING
(see Injury)

BURNS AND SCALDS
(see Injury)

CALLING (persistent)

Females who do not have access to toms and who are
not spayed can suffer periods of perpetual "calling".
This can be very distressing for human and feline alike.

Homoeopathic PULSATILLA 200c, LILIUM TIGRINUM
200c or MUREX 200c once daily can help according to
the nature of the cat. Pulsatilla suits the gentle sort,

CALLING (continued)

Lilium suits the hurried, anxious type and Murex cats usually appear very sad in quiet moments.

Herbally, PASSIFLORA or VALERIAN tincture can help. Two drops twice daily should suffice.

Essential oils of HOPS, SWEET MARJORAM and LAVENDER can exert a calming influence.

CANKER

Canker is a colloquial term loosely meaning any form of ear infection.

Homoeopathic SULPHUR 6c for the cat who avoids warmth or GRAPHITES 6c for the cat who seeks warmth may help. Give once daily.

Cats ears are prone to ear mite infestation and this can be helped by the application of essential oils to the ear opening. CLOVE, LAVENDER, THYME, JUNIPER and ROSEMARY all have beneficial effects in this problem. One drop near the ear opening daily for seven days should suffice. This can be repeated sporadically. If the oils are too strong for your cat's skin they may be diluted using almond or safflower oil.

CAR SICKNESS

Motion sickness can be a very real problem for cats, as can anxiety in the car.

Homoeopathic PETROLEUM 6c or COCCULUS 6c have proved very helpful: give two doses prior to the journey in the preceding half hour.

Essential oils of SWEET FENNEL, PEPPERMINT or CAMO-MILE can exert a calming influence on mind and stomach.

Bach RESCUE REMEDY has often been used with success, two drops as needed.

CATARRH
(see also Influenza and Sneezing)

Acute catarrh can arise from many different viral infections in cats. Chronic catarrh usually arises from an incomplete recovery from such conditions. In these cases there is risk of dehydration and veterinary help should be sought.

Extra VITAMIN C in the diet can help with resistance. In some cats, since catarrh can cause loss of smell, loss of appetite can follow.

Homoeopathic SILICA 6c will help to clear the mucopurulent material. If it is yellow and stringy, KALI. BICH. 6c will also help. If it becomes worse in the evening and is greenish-yellow, PULSATILLA 6c may help. Give once daily.

Herbally, GOLDEN SEAL or MULLEIN tincture can be a very useful treatment.

Essential Oils of EUCALYPTUS, PINE, MYRRH or THYME can be very beneficial in easing congestion.

Tissue Salts of FERR. PHOS., KALI. MUR. and NAT. MUR. will often prove very helpful to restore easier breathing and to decrease congestion.

COLLAPSE

Clearly this is a very serious condition and veterinary help will be needed. However, natural medicines can provide a very useful adjunct to treatment.

CARBO VEGETABILIS 6c is a very useful homoeopathic medicine in this context; give one tablet or two drops of liquid four to six times daily.

Essential oils of PEPPERMINT, JASMINE and ROSEMARY are potent stimulants to the system.

FERR. PHOS. Tissue Salt will help the oxygen-carrying capacity of the blood to aid in recovery.

Bach RESCUE REMEDY has helped many desperate cases recover. Give two drops as often as needed.

CONCUSSION
(see Injury)

CONJUNCTIVITIS

Inflammation of the membranes around the eye can be a very distressing problem. It can follow on from cat "flu" or arise on its own. Chlamydia infection may also be involved.

Extra VITAMIN C in the diet can help with recovery. Homoeopathic EUPHRASIA tincture, a few drops in an eggcupful of boiled, cooled water, can be invaluable applied to the eye. EUPHRASIA 6c tablets, one twice daily by mouth, can also help. If there is oedema in the conjunctiva, APIS 6c one tablet three times daily will be needed. HYDRASTIS 6c will help if there is a yellow purulent discharge. Give one tablet twice daily.

Herbal tinctures of MARIGOLD, EYEBRIGHT or GOLDEN SEAL, two drops twice daily by mouth, will aid healing.

CONSTIPATION

This can be a complicated problem in the cat and veterinary help should be sought if it persists.

MILK OF MAGNESIA can be used but prolonged use will

make the bowel lazy and will deplete the body of minerals.

LIQUID PARAFFIN lubricates a dry stool but it is dangerous if used long term as it can deplete the body of Vitamins A, D and E.

Homoeopathy can provide help. SEPIA 30c can be used when large stools are expelled with difficulty. NUX VOMICA 30c is recommended when stools are dark and knotty. Give twice daily.

Herbal preparations of RHUBARB are gentle laxatives. Tissue Salts: KALI. MUR., CALC. FLUOR. and SILICA will often prove helpful.

CONVALESCENCE

After prolonged illness the system needs some support to aid full recovery.

Homoeopathically PHOSPHORIC ACID 6c, one tablet twice daily, is very useful. CINCHONA 30c, one tablet once daily, may also help.

CONVALESCENCE (continued)

Herbally, the tonic influence of ROSEMARY and OATS is beneficial.

Essential oils of ROSEMARY, SAGE and JASMINE have enlivening properties and can aid recovery from illness.

Tissue Salts of CALC. PHOS., FERR. PHOS. and KALI. PHOS. help to restore vitality to tissues during conva-lescence and can provide invaluable assistance.

COUGH

Since coughs can arise from many causes, veterinary diagnosis may be essential.

Help can be provided by homoeopathic IPECACUANHA 6c if the cough is spasmodic and repetitive; LOBELIA 6c if the cough is asthmatic in sound and appears to come from the throat; SPONGIA 6c if there is heart involvement, and PULSATILLA 6c if the cough is change-able and worse in the evening. Give three times daily.

Herbally, coughs can be soothed by GRINDELIA if the

cough is asthmatic in sound or MULLEIN if there is
mucus. Two drops of tincture three times daily.

Essential oils of CEDARWOOD, EUCALYPTUS or HYSSOP
can be a very useful aid to therapy.

MAG. PHOS. and KALI. SULPH. in Biochemic Tissue Salt
form may prove helpful.

CRUSH INJURY
(see Injury)

CUTS
(see Injury)

CYSTITIS

Cats are commonly affected by this often very painful
and distressing condition. Symptoms are repetitive
journeys to the litter tray, straining at urination,
yowling with pain at times, sometimes with blood
appearing in the urine. In severe cases neat blood can

CYSTITIS (continued)

be passed repeatedly. Repeated antibiotics help
temporarily but do not lessen the frequency of attacks
and can deplete the system. Natural remedies can
provide a useful boost to resistance and lessen the
frequency and severity of attacks.

Dietary measures should include ensuring adequate
water intake, moistening the food if necessary, and
being especially careful if dried food is used. Magne-
sium content of the diet should not exceed 0.1% of the
dry matter and foods which give rise to an acid urine
should help, e.g. diets rich in METHIONINE AMINO
ACID. AMMONIUM CHLORIDE or SODIUM ACID PHOS-
PHATE can be added to the diet but should only be
done under veterinary supervision. VITAMIN C may
help.

Homoeopathic CANTHARIS 6c is the most likely remedy
to be of value in acute attacks. Give one tablet three
or four times daily in case of attack. CAUSTICUM 30c
or NATRUM MUR. 30c may prevent or lessen further
attacks, give one tablet twice weekly. LYCOPODIUM
30c four times daily can help if there is a liver problem.

Herbally, DANDELION root powder can be very beneficial in prevention. CLEAVERS, COUCH GRASS and

HORSETAIL all can be useful.

Biochemic Tissue Salts may also provide much needed relief. FERR. PHOS. and MAG. PHOS. are the preparations to consider (see also Feline Urological Syndrom).

DANDRUFF

Scales of skin forming white or grey flakes in the coat can be a sign of suboptimal health.

Assuming that underlying disease is ruled out, help can be obtained by adding EVENING PRIMROSE OIL to the diet. WHEAT GERM OIL or VITAMIN E can also be helpful.

Homoeopathically, ARSENICUM 6c or NATRUM MUR. 6c
once daily will help speed the cure.

NETTLE infusion can be a useful herbal medicine and
can even be applied to the coat. KELP added to the
food will aid skin health.

The Biochemic Tissue Salts, KALI. SULPH. along with
SILICA can help coat and skin condition.

DERMATITIS
(see Skin Problems)

DIARRHOEA

Be careful to ensure that dehydration does not ensue
from this condition and seek veterinary help if in
doubt.

Homoeopathy is very effective in controlling or curing
the problem but selection of the correct remedy can
prove difficult. If you suspect bad food may have led
to the problem use ARSENICUM 6c and BAPTISIA 6c. If

DIARRHOEA (continued)

there is great straining at the stool, give MERCURIUS CORROSIVUS 6c. If the stool oozes freely, give ALOE 6c. Remedies can be given up to four times daily.

Herbal remedies of value are MEADOWSWEET, PLANTAIN or CATECHU. SLIPPERY ELM or ARROWROOT POWDER can also be very helpful to soothe and calm the bowel. A 24 hour fast is advisable provided there is sufficient fluid intake.

A combination of CALC. PHOS., KALI. MUR. and KALI. PHOS., in Tissue Salt form, should prove helpful.

After prolonged diarrhoea, refer to Convalescence (q.v.).

EARS
(see Canker and Balance)

ECZEMA
(see Skin Problems)

ENTERITIS
(see Diarrhoea)

EYE ULCER

Cats often suffer injury to the front of the eye, causing an ulcer.

This can be helped very effectively by homoeopathy. MERCURIUS CORROSIVUS 30c - one tablet twice daily for three days then one tablet once daily for a week is invaluable.

EUPHRASIA tincture, diluted - a few drops in an eggcupful of boiled, cooled water - twice daily in the eye, will aid healing.

The healing power of the eye is a source of constant amazement and the influence of these remedies (or others selected by a homoeopathic veterinary surgeon) will usually prevent any need for surgery. Veterinary guidance is essential.

FEAR
(see Anxiety)

FELINE UROLOGICAL SYNDROME
(see also Cystitis)

Homoeopathic HYDRANGEA 6c once daily helps to dissolve deposits. If there is obstruction, SARSAPA-RILLA 6c up to six times daily will help but veterinary assistance may be needed. Do not leave obstruction for many hours without veterinary help.

Herbally you can use HORSETAIL and BEARBERRY.

FIGHTING
(see Abscess)

FLEAS
(see Skin Problems and pages 10-11)

FOOD POISONING

Cats are very susceptible to salmonellosis from spoiled food and can die quickly if severely affected. Veterinary help is a must.

Homoeopathic ARSENICUM 30c one tablet four times daily and BAPTISIA 6c one tablet twice daily are essential.

FOREIGN BODY

To aid the rejection by the body of traumatically implanted objects such as thistles, thorns, needles etc. use homoeopathic SILICA 6c once daily. Surgery can usually be avoided by this means. As abscessation forms, bathing the area with warm, strong, salty water is a valuable aid.

FRACTURES
(see Bone Injury)

GINGIVITIS

Sore gums are usually the result of a depressed immune system, often an after-effect of viral infection (e.g. Calici virus). This is a very troublesome condition but it can be helped to some extent by natural medicines.

Homoeopathic remedies of value are: PHOSPHORUS 6c if there is persistent bleeding from the gums.

MERCURIUS CORROSIVUS 6c if there is plentiful saliva.
NITRIC ACID 6c when ulceration is present. Give one
tablet twice daily.

Herbally, ECHINACEA, tincture, two drops twice daily
will help the immune system. MYRRH and GOLDEN SEAL
infusion bathed on the gums will aid healing and
soothe pain. These can provide an effective antiseptic
too.

GLANDS

If your cat's glands are swollen in the throat or neck
area this can indicate deep underlying disease. It is
recommended that you seek veterinary advice for the
problem. However, natural remedies can aid health and
measures of value are:

Homoeopathic BARYTA CARB. 30c one tablet daily.
PULSATILLA 30c one tablet daily if the swellings
fluctuate.

Herbal ECHINACEA tincture, two drops twice daily as
an immune stimulant. Herbal POKE ROOT, tincture two
drops once daily.

GRAZES
(see Injury)

GUMS
(see Gingivitis)

GUNSHOT WOUNDS

Since there is a very real injury incurred, seek veterinary advice but homoeopathic ARNICA 30c three times daily in the early stages is essential. This can be helped by LEDUM 6c, one tablet once daily. If there is need for surgery to remove the projectile, one tablet of STAPHISAGRIA 30c three times daily along with Arnica will help recovery. If nerves are damaged or there is severe pain consider HYPERICUM 6c, three times daily.

HAEMORRHAGE
(see Bleeding)

HAIR BALL

Hair ball ingestion occurs often as a result either of obsessive overgrooming by the cat or of skin problems.

HAIR BALL (continued)

The cat may loose his appetite and become morose.
MILK OF MAGNESIA or LIQUID PARAFFIN may help the
passing of the obstruction but see warnings about
these medications under Constipation (q.v.).

The hair ball can often be vomited with the help of
NUX VOMICA 30c. Give one tablet twice daily.

HAIR LOSS
(see Alopecia)

HEAD INJURY
(see Injury)

HEATSTROKE

This can be an emergency situation calling for rapid
veterinary assistance. The cat can become recumbent
with rapid panting, may collapse and may even become
comatose if heat exposure is too great for too long.

Extreme heatstroke can lead to death.

However, the homoeopathic remedies ACONITUM 30c and GLONOINIUM 30c are essential aids to recovery. Give one tablet as often as every five minutes until recovery starts.

Bach RESCUE REMEDY may also help.

INFLUENZA
(see also Catarrh and Sneezing)

Cat 'flu is a potentially hazardous viral infection and affects eyes, nose, throat and possibly chest.
Calicivirus and Feline Rhinotracheitis virus are the two common viral agents.

Homoeopathic treatment is according to the signs

shown but remedies of value are: PULSATILLA 6c where the symptoms are worse in the evening and there is little or no thirst, and discharges are greenish-yellow. NATRUM MUR. 6c where discharges are generally clear or whitish and there is a tendency to hide and keep warm - there is often a thirst in this case; APIS MEL. 6c where eyes are swollen and puffy and ALLIUM CEPA 6c where eyes are constantly streaming profuse tears. One tablet twice or three times daily should suffice.

Herbally, ECHINACEA tincture, two drops two or three times daily is a very useful adjunct to treatment. If there is much mucus MULLEIN tincture will help.

KALI. MUR., KALI. SULPH. and NAT. MUR. in combination, as Biochemic Tissue Salts, will help the cat to fight off the symptoms of feline influenza.

INJURY

Homoeopathic ARNICA 30c is always useful in any case of injury, wherever it is on the body and howsoever caused. However other homoeopathic remedies are helpful in special circumstances. Remedies can be given at a frequency varying from once daily to hourly,

INJURY (continued)

depending upon the severity of the injury.

1. Bruising - ARNICA 30c.

2. Cuts and Lacerations - HYPERICUM 6c, STAPHISAGRIA 6c. Diluted HYPERICUM and CALENDULA lotion maybe applied to the wounds.

3. Grazes and Abrasions - HYPERICUM 6c. Diluted HYPERICUM and CALENDULA lotion on the injury.

4. Bites - (see Abscess)

5. Crush Injury - HYPERICUM 6c. Diluted HYPERICUM and CALENDULA LOTION if the skin is broken. ARNICA LOTION if the skin is unbroken.

6. Scratches - diluted HYPERICUM and CALENDULA lotion on the injuries.

7. Puncture wounds - LEDUM 6c.

8. Burns and Scalds - CANTHARIS 30c, URTICA 6c.

9. Head Injury and Concussion - NATRUM SULPHURICUM 6c.

10. Eye - SYMPHYTUM 6c, if injury is to eyeball or orbital area. EUPHRASIA 6c and LEDUM 6c if injury is to cornea.

11. Back Injury (see Back Problems)

12. Bone (see Bone Injury)

13. Joint Injury (see Sprains)

14. Hæmorrhage (see Bleeding)

15. Surgical Injury - STAPHISAGRIA 30c.

These remedies may even be given as often as once every five or ten minutes, depending upon the severity of the symptoms. The frequency should be reduced when the cat responds.

JEALOUSY

One tablet daily of the homoeopathic remedy
LACHESIS 200c can help with this condition. Sometimes, there is more resentment mixed with the
jealousy in which case NATRUM MUR. 200c or
STAPHISAGRIA 200c will help. The same dosage is
suggested.

Essential oils of SWEET MARJORAM or LEMON BALM will aid such problems.

The Bach Flower remedy HOLLY can be very useful in this situation.

JOINT INJURY
(see Sprains)

KIDNEY PROBLEMS

Kidney trouble is a very severe and life-threatening condition. The cat may display an increased thirst, the coat becomes dull and loses its condition, the breath may be smelly and dehydration may follow. In severe cases collapse can occur. Natural therapies must be directed to limiting damage and stimulating activity of remaining active kidney tissue. The danger is that

damage has often gone very far before symptoms
become obvious. Seek veterinary help.

Homoeopathic MERCURIUS SOLUBILIS 6c may be a
good remedy with which to start treatments while you
are seeking help. Give once daily.

LABOUR
(see Birth)

LACERATIONS
(see Injury)

LACTATION

If lactation is deficient when suckling kittens, homoeopathic remedies can be very valuable. URTICA 30c
twice daily promotes milk flow. PULSATILLA 200c
three times in one day promotes the desire to nurse
properly. BRYONIA 30c four times daily will help if
there is mastitis. SEPIA 200c twice daily for one or two
days helps if the mother appears indifferent or even
aggressive to her kittens.

Herbally, MILKWORT, MILK THISTLE or GOATS RUE will
all help promote milk flow.

If lactation persists after weaning, IGNATIA 200c once
daily for two days can help. Also URTICA 6x will help
to dry up the mammary glands. This may be given
once or twice daily.

Herbal DANDELION tincture by mouth may help.

LAMENESS
(see Sprains, Injury, Rheumatism, Abscess)

LIVER PROBLEMS

The liver is a vital organ and, as such, problems of liver function are potentially very serious. The liver is the metabolic centre for the body and malfunction here leads to a breakdown of the chemistry involved in carbohydrate, fat and protein metabolism. It is also an excretory organ so toxicity may follow. The first sign is usually loss of appetite. Veterinary help should be sought if in doubt.

Homoeopathic CHELIDONIUM 6x or LYCOPODIUM 30c are very helpful for the liver, especially the former if there is jaundice. CARDUUS 6c may help if the liver is swollen leading to oedema of the abdomen. NUX VOMICA 30c helps if there has been intake of over-rich food. Dosage should be one to four times daily depending on severity.

Herbally, the liver is helped by CENTAURY, DANDELION, BLUE FLAG and YELLOW DOCK.

Essential Oils of CARROT SEED and ROSEMARY can be helpful in stimulating correct liver function.

Bach Flower VERVAIN can help particularly if there is a bad-tempered mental picture.

MASTITIS
(see Lactation)

METRITIS

If there is infection in the womb after giving birth to
kittens the cat can be helped by CAULOPHYLLUM 30c,

METRITIS (continued)

one tablet twice daily followed by SABINA 6c, one
tablet twice daily. If there is a danger to overall health,
veterinary help may be needed.

Herbal remedies of value in treating womb infections
are GOLDEN SEAL, GRATIOLA and MYRRH.

MIDDLE AND INNER EAR PROBLEMS
(see Balance)

MILIARY ECZEMA
(see Skin Problems)

MOUTH
(see Gingivitis)

NAILS

Where the cat's claws do not grow correctly , splits
and flaky or fragile nails can result. Clip them, or use a
scratch patch or emery board.

GRAPHITES 6c given once daily is the homoeopathic
remedy most likely to help in such situations. If there is
a long term nutritional problem SILICA 6c given twice

NAILS (continued)

daily may help. If vaccination is suspected as a possible cause, THUJA 30c once daily may help.

These remedies should be given for a few days only and await results, since nails do not grow instantaneously. Remedies may be repeated weekly after this.

Cats with access to the outside usually have little problem with their claws. Claws for indoor cats can be kept in good order by use of a scratch pad or rustic log in the cat's room. Older cats may need their claws trimmed as they can become caught in clothing, carpets, furniture, etc. owing to weaker foot muscles (they find it more difficult to retract their claws). Declawing of cats cannot be considered humane practise.

OBESITY

Obesity may be a sign of Thyroid trouble, overfeeding, other hormonal problems or of excessive drug treatments.

Clearly, if excessive food intake or unbalanced diet is the cause, steps must be taken to ensure rectification of dietary factors. Advice may be needed here but, in

OBESITY (continued)

general, proprietary "slimming" foods are merely a way of feeding indigestible material effectively to reduce intake of nutrients without reducing overall food intake. This could be considered an expensive route to limiting food intake.

The homoeopathic remedy CALCAREA CARB. 30c - one tablet daily - can help in the battle to lose weight. THYROID 6c once daily may also help.

Herbally, BLADDERWRACK may be very helpful in stimulating the thyroid gland.

If drug usage has led to obesity then homoeopathic NUX VOMICA 30c once daily can prove beneficial, as too can herbal ECHINACEA or DANDELION.

OEDEMA

Oedema is accumulation of fluid in the tissues or body spaces.

If the oedema is in the abdomen and caused by Feline

Infectious Peritonitis then it is essential you have
veterinary help as soon as possible in finding the
correct homoeopathic medication. The outlook is not
good in such cases but homoeopathy does provide a
chance if the cat is not too ill at the start of the
treatment. If thirst is limited, homoeopathic APIS 6c
twice daily will prove useful in promoting fluid reduction. If there is a marked thirst, then ACETIC ACID 6c
or EEL SERUM 6x twice daily will help.

If it is due to accumulation of fluid in the body from
poor circulation or deficient kidney function (usually
only identifed by a vet), then herbal DANDELION
tincture should prove very helpful.

OIL CONTAMINATION

Cats do get into some silly scrapes and occasionally
this can prove serious. Sump oil, diesel oil or fuel oil
can be very toxic and can damage the skin. It is not
uncommon for cats to become contaminated by these
agents or to fall into containers of one or other of
them. In addition to very prompt, careful and thorough
washing under veterinary guidance, the homoeopathic
remedy PETROLEUM 30c is very useful in limiting

OIL CONTAMINATION (continued)

toxicity. Give twice daily for a week.

In order to help the body to detoxify, VITAMIN C supplementation and DANDELION tincture will be useful additions to therapy.

PANIC
(see Anxiety)

PARALYSIS
(see Back Problems)

PERSISTENT CALLING
(see Calling)

PINING
(see Bereavement)

POISONING

Wherever ingestion of noxious chemicals has occurred, natural therapy forms a useful stimulus to detoxification.

Homoeopathic NUX VOMICA 30c given three times daily will assist the liver to metabolise the poisons. ECHINACEA 6x given twice daily is also a valuable aid to detoxification. A homoeopathic potency of the chemical itself may also be of help in the recovery phase.

Herbally, GARLIC, ECHINACEA and DANDELION tinctures form a very useful adjunct to therapy.

Essential oils of SWEET FENNEL will also help to purify the blood.

POST OPERATIVE CARE
(see also Injury)

If your cat has had to undergo surgery for any reason it will have been subjected to trauma and to anaesthetic agents. These are a necessary "side-effect" of the efforts to help your cat surgically. To help your cat recover fully from anaesthesia, see Poisoning.
The resultant mental and physical trauma can be helped by homoeopathic ARNICA 30c given four times daily and STAPHISAGRIA 30c given twice daily.

Herbally, COMFREY tincture can be of help.

PREGNANCY
(see also Birth)

Strict attention to correct dietary intake is very important. The developing kittens *in utero* are vulnerable to all changes and influences put upon the mother. Stress, dietary changes, dietary errors, vaccination, viral infections etc. can all have an adverse effect and should be avoided if at all possible. Any problems should be treated promptly by natural medicine, particularly homoeopathy, since it is so safe. Some

PREGNANCY (continued)

herbs and many essential oils should be avoided
during pregnancy. For the sake of safety, avoid these
unless you have expert knowledge (for exceptions see
Birth q.v.).

Homoeopathic CAULOPHYLLUM 30c can be given
towards the end of pregnancy to prepare for the birth.
Give twice weekly for the last three weeks. CALCAREA
PHOS. 30c may be given weekly throughout pregnancy
to help the kittens' skeletal development.

Herbal RASPBERRY LEAF is a useful tonic for pregnant
queens and tincture or tablets of this can be given
daily during the last week of pregnancy.

PUNCTURE WOUNDS
(see Injury)

RESENTMENT

Cats can be very resentful animals. They can object to
changes in home life, in environment, in companions, in
food, etc.

STAPHISAGRIA 200c or NATRUM MUR. 200c once daily
are the homoeopathic remedies which most often help.

RESENTMENT (continued)

Essential oils of LAVENDER, BERGAMOT, SANDALWOOD and YLANG YLANG can help.

Bach Flower WILLOW can be of great help.

RESPIRATORY DISEASE
(see Catarrh, Cough)

RHEUMATISM

Rheumatism is a very unspecific term for muscle stiffness.

Give the homoeopathic remedy RHUS TOX. 6c once daily, if you suspect rheumatism.

Herbal DEVILS CLAW may also help.

RHINITIS
(see Catarrh)

RINGWORM

Ringworm in cats is reported to be a very difficult condition to cure, however natural medicine methods do seem to be able to solve the problem in most cases. It is not a worm infestation, as its name may imply, but a fungal infection of the skin.

Adequate nutrition is essential to combat chronic ringworm in cats whether they be single or in a colony. VITAMINS C and A are perhaps the most important vitamins to watch and minerals such as IODINE, ZINC, SULPHUR and SELENIUM play a very important role in skin and hair health. The dose rate of supplementation is crucial and expert advice should be sought.

Homoeopathic KALI. ARSENICUM 30c is a first line treatment. BACILLINUM 30c is a help in building resistance to the disease. Give once daily. However, qualified veterinary homoeopathic advice is recommended since this disease is infectious to the cat's human companions.

RINGWORM (continued)

Herbally, MARIGOLD tincture will help build resistance and aid skin health. YELLOW DOCK and BLUE FLAG may form a useful addition.

Essential oils to help build resistance and to discourage fungal infections are MYRRH, TEA TREE and SPIKE LAVENDER.

ROAD ACCIDENT
(see Injury)

RODENT ULCER

This is a very troublesome condition of immune mal-function in cats and affects the upper lips in most cases. Lesions can appear elsewhere on the skin and feet. These latter lesions are usually moist and weep a whitish exudate.

Homoeopathic NATRUM MUR. 30c, NITRIC ACID 30c, or MERCURIUS SOLUBILIS 30c are the most commonly prescribed homoeopathic remedies, depending upon the nature of the cat and its reaction to the disease. Natrum suits a cat who, although liking attention, will go off alone when upset; Nitric acid suits the cat which has pain, is irritable and is adverse to noise. Mercurius suits the cat which has a dull appearance but becomes suddenly galvanised by interference, has a wet mouth and is thirsty. Give once daily.

HYPERICUM and CALENDULA LOTION may also be applied to the lesion.

Herbal treatments able to stimulate a return to normal in immune function and to help the body to detoxify are ECHINACEA, DANDELION, BURDOCK, YELLOW DOCK and CLEAVERS.

Essential oils of MYRRH and TEA TREE will be of assistance and may even be diluted and applied sparingly to lesions.

Laser therapy is an invaluable aid to treatment of lesions but experienced veterinary help and advice are needed for this since wavelength, frequency and power are critical.

ROUNDWORMS
(see also Tapeworms and pages 10-11)

While it is well-known that conventional chemical wormers do eliminate a good percentage of the round worms in a cat's bowels, they may also have a deleterious effect on the delicate balance of the body. However, natural compounds for worming are, by contrast, unproven and may also be marginally toxic. If natural methods are sought, care should be exercised and some professional supervision is advisable.

GARLIC is a great deterrent of all parasites and represents a safe effective and wholesome preventive measure. Other herbal remedies are WORMWOOD, PUMPKIN SEEDS, SANTONICA, SOUTHERNWOOD and QUASSIA WOOD.

Homoeopathic preparations of some of these plants go under the name of ABROTANUM, CINA and SANTONINE. A 3x potency of these twice daily for three or four days will be much safer than the herbal preparation but possibly less effective.

SCALDS
(see Injury)

SCRATCHES
(see Injury)

SEXUAL EXCITEMENT
(see also Calling in Females)

A tom who is suffering excess sexual excitement or frustration can be helped by homoeopathic CANTHARIS 30c and TARENTULA HISPANICA 200c. Give twice daily.

Herbal help can be provided in the form of SKULLCAP, VALERIAN or HOPS.

Essential oils of LAVENDER or LEMON BALM are very beneficial. Lavender may also be hung in the room.

Bach Flower ROCKWATER, HOLLY, CHICORY and HEATHER can be very helpful.

SHOCK

Homoeopathy provides great help in the shape of ACONITE 200c, give one tablet as often as needed until effects show.

STAR OF BETHLEHEM or RESCUE REMEDY are Bach Flower remedies of great assistance.

SHOW FRIGHT

GELSEMIUM 200c or ARGENTUM NITRICUM 200c are the homoeopathic remedies best able to help in such problems. With Gelsemium there is a more withdrawn appearance, with Argentum Nit., a fearful approach. Give one tablet of the chosen remedy twice daily the day before a show and on the morning of the show.

Herbally, SKULLCAP, VALERIAN or HOPS can be helpful.

Essential oils of LAVENDER and LEMON BALM will have a great calming effect.

Bach RESCUE REMEDY can be very helpful in such circumstances. Bach CHERRY PLUM or CERATO are single remedies which may help.

KALI. PHOS. is the Biochemic Tissue Salt most likely to prove helpful for cats suffering this problem.

SINUSITIS
(see Catarrh, Influenza and Sneezing)

SKIN PROBLEMS
(see also Dandruff, Alopecia, Allergy, Acne, Ringworm)

Skin problems can take on many and diverse forms, the variety being too much to make a full dissertation in this small book.

However, it is useful to note that SULPHUR 30c, GRAPHITES 30c, NATRUM MUR. 30c and PULSATILLA 30c are the homoeopathic remedies most often prescribed in cases of skin trouble, overall. Sulphur patients tend to avoid warmth, Pulsatilla ones prefer outdoors, Graphites and Natrum Mur. are both for "heat seekers". Give once daily for three days then once or twice weekly.

Milliary Eczema (papulocrustal dermatitis) is often helped, in addition, by FOLLICULINUM 6c or ORCHITINUM 6c.

Herbally, YELLOW DOCK and BLUE FLAG are very useful in clearing the digestive system (especially the liver) and making way for a healthier skin.

Essential oils of ROSEMARY, JUNIPER and THYME are well-known for their antiseptic and anti-inflammatory properties.

A combination of Biochemic Tissue Salts to include CALC. SULPH., KALI. MUR., KALI. SULPH. AND SILICA can prove very helpful in aiding recovery from skin problems in general.

Clearly, if there is a flea problem this must be handled as best one can and herbal deterrents around the house, herbal flea collars (or those containing essential oils), herbal and aromatherapy sprays, etc. can all prove very beneficial in reducing the problem without the worrying toxicity of such chemicals as organophosphorus compounds or organochlorines. These modern chemicals can be very effective but their use is not without danger to cats and people and the "residual" products available represent a hazard of three month's duration. Even pyretherins (modern derivatative of pyrethium) may not be safe. There is a small section discussing flea control in the first section of this book (see pages 10-11).

SNEEZING
(see also Catarrh and Influenza)

Special remedies are homoeopathic EUPHRASIA 6c; or IPECACUANHA 6c if it is spasmodic and repetitive.

SNEEZING (continued)

ALLIUM CEPA 6c is useful if there is a profuse streaming of clear fluid from the eyes. Dosage should be given two or three times daily.

SPINE
(see Back)

SPRAIN

Joint injury in the form of sprains is helped by homoeopathic RUTA GRAV. 6c one tablet three or four times daily, depending upon the severity of the injury. ARNICA 30c may also be useful at the same dose rate. If there is extreme swelling of the joint, APIS 6c, three times daily, will aid the healing.

Herbally, COMFREY tincture is a useful internal medication and Comfrey applications can be an invaluable aid to healing. There has been a scare about Comfrey of late but I leave it up to the reader to sift the evidence for himself or herself and evaluate the case against Comfrey, which has proven valuable for centuries. Rats were fed experimentally with large quantities of Comfrey in Japan and I believe a tumour was found. It was not proven to be the result of feeding Comfrey. Alkaloids known as pyrolizidines have been found in Comfrey, poisonous members of this group of chemicals being found in the dangerous plant Ragwort. The toxicity of Comfrey is much less clear than that of Ragwort and its traditional use has never been shown to be hazardous. It was even used for some cancers in former times.

Application of essential oils of ROSEMARY can provide useful pain relief.

SPRAYING OF URINE
(inappropriate)

This inconvenient, inappropriate behaviour can arise from a number of emotions in the cat. Territorial marking, resentment (q.v.), jealousy (q.v.), fear (q.v.) are among these.

Apart from remedies mentioned under other headings,

SPRAYING OF URINE (continued)

homoeopathic STRAMONIUM 200c or CANTHARIS 200c may help, one tablet to be given daily.

Herbally, SKULLCAP and VALERIAN will tend to lower the desire to spray and HORSETAIL can help the urogenital system.

Essential oils of LAVENDER and LEMON BALM can help and application of these oils or THYME at the favoured site could deter. PEPPERMINT OIL also has the reputation of acting as a deterrent.

STRESS

At times of upheaval, in the family or home, cats can become very stressed.

Homoeopathically STAPHISAGRIA 200c or NUX VOMICA 200c will be likely to relieve the situation. Give once daily for three days.

Herbally, tinctures or tablets of SKULLCAP, VALERIAN, PASSIFLORA or HOPS all have calming properties.

Essential oils of LAVENDER, LEMON BALM and JASMINE are very soothing mentally.

Bach Flower remedies mixed together can provide an insulation against the stress. Use HOLLY, MIMULUS and WALNUT. Bach RESCUE REMEDY may help.

SURGERY

After essential surgery your cat could need help (see Post Operative Care).

TAPEWORMS
(see also Roundworms)

The prefatory remarks made for roundworms (q.v.) apply also in the case of tapeworms (see page 10).

Herbal remedies suggested as possible treatments are: POMEGRANATE and MALE FERN. Both have the reputation of eliminating tapeworms. GARLIC has the reputation as a preventive.

Homoeopathic preparations of the former two are known as GRANATUM and FILIX-MAS. These can be used in a very low potency, such as 3x and may be given twice daily for three or four days.

TEETH/TARTAR
(see also Breath)

FRAGARIA in low potency (e.g. 3x) can provide a homoeopathic aid to oral freshness and can help to prevent tartar formation if used regularly, e.g. twice or three times weekly.

POWDERED DILL seeds and MYRRH are an excellent aid to oral hygiene. A mixed powder can be applied to the gums or a paste can be made from the powder for such application.

Infected tooth roots and gums may be helped by homoeopatic HEPAR SULPH. 30c or MERCURIUS SOL. 30c twice daily.

THROAT

Cats can develop sore throats but this is usually an extension of gingivitis (q.v.).

However, homoeopathic remedies such as PULSATILLA 30c or PHYTOLACCA 30c can help the throat if it is part of an acute infection.   Give one tablet twice daily.

Herbally, tincture of ECHINACEA will be very helpful. Give two or three drops twice daily for three days.

Essential oils such as BERGAMOT, HYSSOP, SAGE and THYME can all provide a very valuable and soothing effect.

The Biochemic Tissue Salts NAT. MUR., FERR. PHOS., and MAG. PHOS. can prove helpful.

THYROID PROBLEMS

Homoeopathy can help both hyper- and hypo-thyroid problems. IODUM 30c is a great regulator of the thyroid; give one tablet daily. THYROIDINUM 6c in hypothyroid situations and THYROIDINUM 30c in

hyperthyroid situations can also help. FLOR DE PIEDRA
6c can also stimulate an under-active thyroid gland.
These should be given once daily.

TONSILLITIS
(see Throat)

TRAVEL SICKNESS
(see Car Sickness)

URINE BLOCKAGE
(see Feline Urological Syndrome)

URINE SPRAYING
(see Spraying)

URINE RETENTION
(see Feline Urological Syndrome)

VACCINATION REACTIONS

Vaccines are given as a challenge to the immune system to sensitise it to certain specific infections so that there should be residual immunity in case of the cat coming into contact with that disease. Unfortunately, the strength of stimulus can be too great in some individuals. Results of this are disturbances in immune function.

VACCINATION REACTIONS (continued)

Should this occur, homoeopathic THUJA 30c once daily
will help plus herbal ECHINACEA tincture or tablets
once daily. After a week, one can move on to a treatment aimed more at any specific symptoms which may
have arisen. Homoeopathic nosodes provide a gentle
method of disease prevention but have not been
tested for efficacy in laboratory conditions (see also
pages 7-10).

VOMITING

One must be wary, with a symptom such as vomiting,
of missing signs of underlying serious disease. Consult
a vet if in doubt. However, simple vomiting can occur
and often no "diagnosis" can be reached. Symptoms
should clear within two or three days or you will
definitely need help.

Homoeopathic PHOSPHORUS 30c, once daily, if food or
drink is vomited within half an hour of intake. NUX
VOMICA 30c if vomiting results from overeating or
from stealing unsuitable food (give three times daily).
If the vomitus is yellow and if there is thirst and a wet

mouth give MERCURIUS SOLUBILIS 30c twice daily or if there is thirst and a dry mouth give ARSENICUM ALBUM 30c twice daily.

Biochemic Tissue Salts may also prove helpful. Consider: NAT. SULPH. if bile is vomited; NAT. PHOS. if sour acid stomach secretions are vomited; KALI. MUR. if thick mucus is vomited; FERR. PHOS. if food is vomited.

WORMS
(see Tapeworms, Roundworms and Ringworm)

WOUNDS
(see Injury)

INDEX